DORK SHADOWS

The Collected Dork Tower, Volume II

by John Kovalic

DORK STORM PRESS

OTHER BOOKS BY JOHN KOVALIC:

Dork Covenant: The Collected Dork Tower Comic Books, I

Dork Shadows: The Collected Dork Tower Comic Books, II

Livin' La Vida Dorka: The Collected Dork Tower Comic Strips, I

Wild Life: The Cardinal Collection

The Wild Life Journals

The Wild Life Files

Dork Storm Press
PO Box 45063,
Madison, WI 53744
http://www.dorkstorm.com

Marketing, sales and advertising inquiries:
sales@dorkstorm.com
Phone: (608) 255-1348 • Fax (608) 442-1528

Editorial and other inquiries:
john@kovalic.com.

Cover design: Phil Reed
Interior design and layout: Aaron Williams

PRINTED IN CANADA • SECOND PRINTING, October 2001 • ISBN 1-930964-41-2

For my Aunt Evalyn and
Uncle Bob,

For the great times, and the
Tastee-Freeze...

DORKS IN BLACK

When John Kovalic asked me to write the introduction to this new Dork Tower collection I told him it would be an honor. With characteristic modesty John insisted the honor would be his. In either case, one thing is clear: John Kovalic is not only one of the most talented people I've ever met, he's probably the hardest working and most dedicated.

Since Sandy Clark first introduced us at Wizardworld Chicago I've been amazed by the breadth of John's published works. Not only does this man write and draw the fine comic book you're currently reading, he also creates daily strips, editorial cartoons, T-shirts, on-line comics, and even helps design games (if you haven't already done so, run out and get "Apples to Apples.")

Despite the wide range and success of his work John remains down-to-earth, just as quick to hand out a compliment as he is to graciously accept one. You can see examples of this attitude through John's convention appearances and in his e-mail newsletter as he promotes work he respects, no matter who created it, just because he feels it's the right thing to do.

But it's most likely not John's hard work and sterling personal qualities that led you to Dork Tower - it was probably the talent so wonderfully expressed in these pages. When creating a humor series about SF fans, Goths, muskrats, and gamers it would be terribly easy to rely solely on inside jokes and obscure references but through Dork Tower John manages to show the basic humanity of geeks and the basic geekness of humanity.

What more can I say without embarrassing John more than his appearance in National Enquirer? Just this: if you're reading this introduction you need this book, it's for you and about you. After all, only geeks read introductions (and only bigger geeks write them!)

Lowell Cunningham
-Creator, *"Men In Black"*

"God bless us, every one!"

-Tiny Tim,
A Christmas Carol

"God save my little broken body."

-Rizzo the Rat in
A Muppet Christmas Carol

CHRISTMASTIME IS HERE... HAPPINESS AND CHEER.

TIME FOR ALL THAT CHILDREN CALL... THE GREATEST TIME OF YEAR

gRuMbLe

A VERY DORKY CHRISTMAS
by JOHN KOVALIC

CHRISTMAS, HUMBUG! A TIME OF GREED AND PURE, BLIND MATERIALISM! ALL PEOPLE WANT IS STUFF! STUFF, STUFF, STUFF!

STUFF HERE! STUFF HERE! GETCHER STUFF HERE!

OH, WELL. AT LEAST THERE'S ONE THING THAT'S PURE AND TRUE...

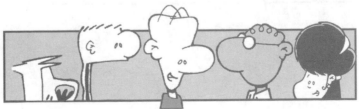

THE LATEST "TRAVAILLER" SUPPLEMENT FROM GTW GAMES! ‹DROOL›

MUST... HAVE... IT! ‹DROOL SLOBBER›

BUT FIRST, "HACK 'N' SLAY" MAGAZINE, WITH HARD-HITTING INDUSTRY NEWS, HONEST REVIEWS AND BALANCED SCENARIOS.

...AND PICS OF CHICKS IN CHAIN-MAIL BIKINIS, OF COURSE...

GTW GAMES TO CLOSE!

GTW Games, of "Travailler" fame, is bankrupt and will never EVER print another game, according to industry so... CEO Frank ...: a fork in us: ...rn out the lights. ...Like we even had a chance.

BLINK BLINK

NOOOOOOOO

SAY... ISN'T THAT MATT?

CAN'T BE. HE'S FIVE MILES AWAY AT PEGASAURUS GAMES NOW...

THIS IS A TRAGEDY! THIS IS A TRAVESTY! **THIS IS THE END OF CHRISTMAS AS WE KNOW IT!**

MISTER...

HAVE YOU FORGOTTEN WHAT CHRISTMAS IS ABOUT?

"IN THE FIELDS CLOSE BY THERE WERE SHEPHERDS WHO WATCHED THEIR FLOCKS BY NIGHT.

"THE ANGEL OF THE LORD APPEARED TO THEM AND THE GLORY OF THE LORD SHONE AROUND THEM. AND THE ANGEL SAID 'BE NOT AFRAID.

"'I BRING YOU TIDINGS OF GREAT JOY. TODAY IN THE TOWN OF DAVID A SAVIOR HAS BEEN BORN TO YOU.'"

"AND WISE MEN FROM THE EAST SAW THE CHILD WITH HIS MOTHER MARY, AND OFFERED HIM GIFTS OF GOLD, FRANKINCENSE AND MYRRH.'"

WOW.

YOU'RE RIGHT.

LIKE THE SHEPHERDS, I SHOULD ACCEPT THE JOY OF THE SEASON. AND LIKE THE WISE MEN, I SHOULD ACCEPT THAT...

THERE'S **LOTS** OF COOL GIFTS TO **GET!** WOO-WOO!

FORGET IT...

18

20

21

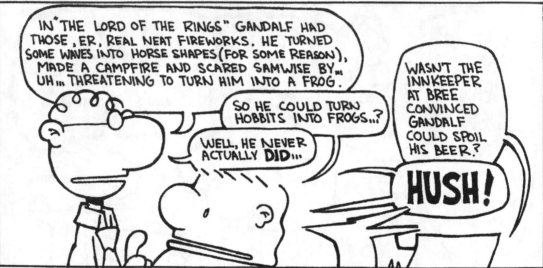

OK! OK! SETTLE DOWN, EVERYONE.

WE'VE GOT TO FIGURE OUT WHAT TO **DO** HERE!

YOU'RE RIGHT!

CARSON! HURRY! LET ME SEE GANDALF'S **CHARACTER SHEET!**

OK.

GENTLEMEN, I **BELIEVE** THIS WIZARD MAY BE OF SOME USE TO US AFTER ALL!

HUZZAH!

LATER

...YES, TECHNICALLY I **SUPPOSE** YOU **COULD** THEORETICALLY USE GANDALF AS A **BATTERING RAM** ...AGAIN... ≷WHIMPER≷

HUZZAH! TAKE **THAT,** BLACK GATE OF CIRITH GORGOR!

WHOAH! DON'T BOGART THAT WIZARD, MR. GREEDY! I'M STILL USING HIM AS A SHIELD!

TELL ME ...ONCE CRITICAL HITS REACH TRIPLE DIGITS, DO YOU GET A DISCOUNT ON SAVING ROLLS...?

RESEARCH BY BERKLAV LORR PETER DELLORTO

THE **END!** WOO!

23

DORK TOWER
BY JOHN KOVALIC

OK... SO WHAT DO WE HAVE HERE... TWO "GALOOB" LAND SPEEDERS, ON SALE...

SOME MICROMACHINE ...UH... "TUSKEN RAIDERS," IMPERIAL PILOTS AND TEEEENY TINY EWOKS. HE HE HE. HOW ADORABLE...

"STAR WARS: THE PHANTOM MENACE" ACTION FIGURES... OH... ALMOST MISSED THE BABYLON FIVE SPACESHIPS IN YOUR CART THERE...

OOO! I DIDN'T EVEN **KNOW** THAT THEY MADE BARBIE AND KENS DRESSED UP AS "STAR TREK" CHARACTERS, OR XENA AND GABRIELLE **DOLLS**!

AND **SIX** "PRINCESS LEIA AS JABBA THE HUTT'S CAPTIVE IN HIS LAIR" LIMITED EDITION ACTION FIGURE DIORAMAS. NEAT.

SO, HOW OLD ARE YOUR KIDS?

TOYS ARE WE!

LET'S SEE... IGOR'S TWENTY-SIX, AND MATT HERE IS...

I AM **NEVER** GOING TO GET A DATE IF WOMEN SCREAM WHENEVER MY HOBBIES ARE BROUGHT UP...

TECHNICALLY, SHE DIDN'T REALLY **NEED** TO CALL SECURITY, YOU KNOW...

OOOO! JAR JAR BINKS WITH THE SPECIAL KUNG-FU GRIP EARS! CAN WE GO BACK SOON? CAN WE? HUH? HUH? HUH?

DORK TOWER BY JOHN KOVALIC

=AHEM= WE HERE AT 'DORK TOWER' WOULD LIKE TO UPDATE YOU ON SOME CHANGES HERE IN THE MAGAZINE.

YES.

IT'S TRAGIC! HORRIBLE! MIND-BOGGLING! IT'S OVER!

=SIGH= WE'RE TAKING A BREAK, FOLKS.

IT'S DOOM! DARKNESS! DISASTER!

SHADIS IS ON HIATUS, SO WE'RE TAKING A VACATION...

THE DREAM IS GONE! DESTROYED! FORGOTTEN! IT'S OVER, OVER OVER!

=SOB=

BUT YOU CAN NOW FIND DORK TOWER IN OUR BEST SELLING BIMONTHLY COMIC BOOK, 'DORK TOWER.'

AND YOU CAN KEEP UP WITH DORK TOWER AT HTTP://DORK TOWER.COM. SO DON'T WORRY. THERE ARE LOTS OF WAYS TO SPEND THE INTERIM.

AND IT SEEMS TO ME, YOU ♫ LIVED YOUR LIFE LIKE A CANDLE IN ♫ THE WIIND...

DRINKING HEAVILY, FOR EXAMPLE...

DORK TOWER

8

HIGH SOBRIETY

"Great spirits have always faced violent protest from mediocre minds."

- *Albert Einstein*

"I will be the greatest pokémon trainer...the greatest pokémon master...of all time!"

- *Ash Ketchum, Pokemon*

PEGASAURUS GAMES

YES, **FRIDAY,** YOU MERCHANT OF SATANISM, YOU PEDDLER OF PROFANE **PUTREFACTION,** YOU...

SORRY. FRIDAY'S NO GOOD.

UH... WHAT?

FRIDAY WE'RE BEING PICKETED BY "MOTHERS AGAINST EVERYTHING." SATURDAY, "MINISTERS APPALLED BY ROLEPLAYING" ARE SCHEDULED FOR A SIT-IN. SUNDAY WE'RE **CLOSED,** BUT "COLLECTIBLE CARD GAMERS AGAINST PRICE GOUGING" WILL BE PROTESTING, NEVERTHE-LESS.

NEXT WEEK IS BOOKED SOLID BY MUNDANES WHO HATE GOTHS, GOTHS WHO HATE MUNDANES, AND TRAIN-GAMERS (WHO DON'T REALLY HATE ANYBODY, BUT FEEL LEFT OUT). **THEN** THERE ARE THE CLASHES BETWEEN ROLEPLAYERS, CARD GAMERS AND COMIC COLLECTORS TO FIT IN.

OH! AND I ALMOST FORGOT THE **FURRIES.**

MMMM...

HOW ABOUT THURSDAY, JUNE 18th? DOES THAT WORK FOR...

NEVERMIND...

ESCAPE FROM ELB

BOX OFFICE

POISON

BURN PIKACHU BURN!

WELL, SURPRISE, **SURPRISE.**

WHAT?

OH, YET **ANOTHER** NEWSPAPER ARTICLE GETTING EVERYTHING WRONG ABOUT **GAMERS.**

I MEAN, TREKKERS, COMICS FANBOYS, GAMERS, COLLECTORS— ANY TIME THE MEDIA TACKLES **ANY** ASPECT OF FANDOM, THEY MAKE US OUT TO BE SUCH **LOSERS!**

SO?

SO I'M **TIRED** OF IT! WHY CAN'T THE MEDIA GIVE **US** THE KIND OF INFORMED, UNBIASED, INTELLIGENT, **SERIOUS** COVERAGE THEY GIVE TO...

SOMETHING WILL COME! **SOMETHING WILL COME!**

AS LONG AS YOU'RE NOT HOLDING YOUR BREATH, I SUPPOSE I SHOULDN'T BE CONCERNED WITH YOUR HEALTH...

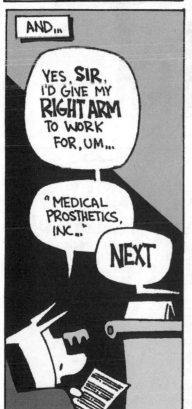

42

COUNTER, DEMONSTRATION? OOOO, I'D AVOID **THAT** AT **ALL** COSTS, IF I WAS YOU.

WHAT ON EARTH FOR?

IGOR! THE PRESS JUST **LOOKS** FOR A WAYS TO MAKE US LOOK **RIDICULOUS!** THEY GO OUT OF THEIR **WAY** TO DO IT! DO WE **NEED** THE HASSLE?

DO WE **WANT** TO BE PORTRAYED AS **WEIRDOS** AND **IDIOTS**? AS **FREAKS** AND **GEEKS**? DO WE **WANT** TO LOOK LIKE **FOOLS**?

MORE THAN USUAL, YOU MEAN?

YES, AND ANYWAY, WHAT DOES A **POKÉMON** PROTEST HAVE TO DO WITH **ME?**

I'M **SICK** OF THOSE FURRY LITTLE FREAKS.

MATT! THINK ABOUT IT!

THIS ISN'T **JUST** ABOUT POKÉMON! IT'S ABOUT **GAMING!** THINK HOW THIS AFFECTS **YOU!** THINK WHAT **YOU** SHOULD BE **DOING!**

POKÉMON CARDS ARE BURNING! WE'VE GOT TO BE PREPARED!

RIGHT!

I'LL GET THE MARSHMALLOWS.

LET'S GO OVER THAT AGAIN...

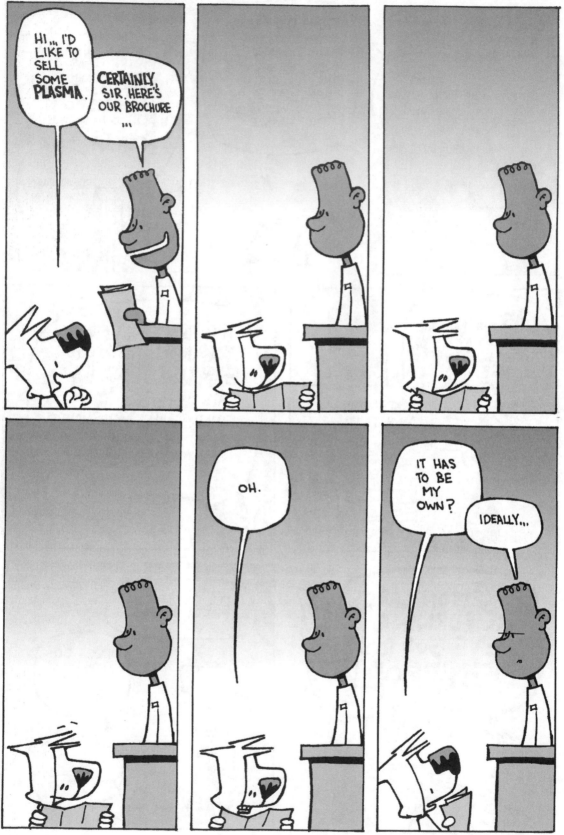

44

45

C'MON, MATT! LET'S GET IN SOME FACES!

YOU KNOW, IGOR, I'M HAVING A **HARD** TIME GETTING BEHIND A **STUPID** GAME FOR **STUPID** PEOPLE. IT'S GOT **STUPID** MECHANICS AND **STUPID** RULES AND IS **FULL** OF STUPID, STUPID ...UH...

...STUPID... ...WELL... OTHER STUFF...

YOU'VE NEVER PLAYED IT, HAVE YOU?

WHAT'S **THAT** GOT TO DO WITH ANYTHING?

≥SIGH≤

OK. WHY ARE YOU PEOPLE BURNING POKÉMON CARDS?

WHY?

BECAUSE POKÉMON IS **EVIL**! IT'S A PRODUCT OF THE **DEVIL**! IT'S A **SIGN** OF THE **END** OF THE **WORLD**!!!

HUFF ≥OOF≤ TOSS

YA KNOW, WHEN THEY'VE GOT A POINT, THEY'VE GOT A...

MATT!

46

47

BUT FIRST, THERE'S **JUSTICE** TO METE OUT!

OOOOH, **YEAH**. LET'S RUSH **ALL** THOSE PHOTOGENIC FANBOYS IN FRONT OF THE CAMERAS!

I MEAN, LET'S **FACE** IT: WE'LL **NEVER** BE ACCEPTED, SO WHY EVEN **TRY**? CAN YOU **IMAGINE** ANYTHING MORE **RIDICULOUS** OR **HUMILIATING** THAN A GROUP OF **ANGRY GAMERS** ON PAGE ONE OF **MUD BAY TODAY**?

THEY'LL BE **LAUGHING STOCKS**!

MATT! THIS PROTEST IS TOO **INSIDIOUS** TO **IGNORE**! IT'S **CRITICAL** WE STAND UP AGAINST IT!

I'M SORRY, IGOR, BUT I REALLY JUST DON'T **CARE**!

FOR A START, I'M **SICK** OF POKÉMON, ITS HYPE AND ITS OVEREXPOSURE! SECONDLY, I DON'T EVEN **PLAY** POKÉMON, SO WHY SHOULD PEOPLE BURNING IT BOTHER ME?

I'VE **BETTER THINGS** TO DO, YOU KNOW! I READ GREAT LITERATURE, LISTEN TO ROCK MUSIC, COLLECT COMIC BOOKS... I **DO** HAVE A **LIFE**!

SO, SINCE **NOTHING** HERE AFFECTS ME AT **ALL** ...!

WE NEED MORE KINDLING. GET SOME GREAT LITERATURE, ROCK CDs AND COMIC BOOKS...

48

49

AND THAT'S **INSPIRING**. SINCERITY HAS GENIUS, POWER AND **MAGIC** TO IT.

IT'S THE MAGIC OF BEING **TRUE** TO YOUR-**SELF**, OF KEEPING YOUR **INTEGRITY**! IT'S THE MAGIC THAT LETS **EACH** OF **US** HOLD ON TO OUR **DIGNITY**!

WOW.

THANKS.

SO. FANCY A GAME OF POKÉMON? IT ACTUALLY LOOKS PRETTY COOL, YOU KNOW...

WHEN I GET A BREAK. THE MEN'S ROOM'S BACKED UP AGAIN. FIRST I HAVE TO FIND A LARGER PLUNGER. AND A SNORKEL...

THE END! PIKA PIKA

"If we get through for two minutes
only, it will be a start..."

The Jam, "Start"

"I must hurry back to my comic book store, where I dispense the insults rather than absorb them."

- Comic Book Guy, The Simpsons

DORK TOWER

BY JOHN KOVALIC

8:10 AM, **PEGASAURUS GAMES**, MUD BAY. BILL BLYDEN, MANAGER, ARRIVES AT THE STORE.

8:31 AM

AIEEEE! GOTTA RESTOCK! GOTTA REORDER! GOTTA JUGGLE INVENTORY. GOTTA SWEEP, CLEAN AND MOP! GOTTA **PANIC!**

9:56 AM

HELLO, MANUFACTURERS? HELLO, DISTRIBUTORS? HELLO, SUPPLIERS? HELLO, BANK? HELLO, ANTACID SHIPMENT?

12:03 PM

I **KNOW** I'M THE ONLY HELP YOU HAVE, BUT I NEED MONDAY OFF, TUESDAY OFF, WEDNESDAY OFF, THURSDAY O...

1:13 PM

...DAY OFF AND THE FOLLOWING TUESDAY OFF.

I ALSO NEED A PAY RAISE

3:11 PM

HAS THAT SPECIAL ORDER OF $319.50 WORTH OF NONRETURNABLE WARHAMSTER ROLEPLAYING SUPPLEMENTS COME IN?

YEEES...

I DON'T WANT THEM ANYMORE.

4:32 PM

ONCE I PAY THE BILLS... COVER RENT... SATISFY CREDITORS... AND SELL PLASMA... I **MIGHT** BE ABLE TO **EAT** THIS WEEK...

5:18 PM

WOW. SO YOU RUN A **GAMING** STORE.

BEATS WORKING, I GUESS...

SOB

55

DORK ↑ TOWER

BY JOHN KOVALIC

SUPPRESSED TRANSMISSION
The First Broadcast
by Kenneth Hite

JUST IN!

STEVE JACKSON GAMES

MAXWELL! IT LOOKS LIKE YOU'VE GOT HALF OF THE "GORYHAWK" SETTING THERE.

YES! AND THE REST WILL SOON BE MINE, TOO!))

IT'S SO KEWL, IT MUST BE MINE! I MUST OWN EVERY SUPPLEMENT! I MUST OWN EVERY SOURCEBOOK!

HAVEN'T WE BEEN THROUGH THIS BEFORE?

NO! THIS IS NEW! HOT! FRESH! A REVELATION IN GAMING!

LIKE YOU SAID ABOUT "OL' HADIM", "DORK SUN" AND "PAIN-SCAPE," RIGHT?

THAT WAS A DIFFERENT TIME. THAT WAS A DIFFERENT PLACE!

THAT WAS WHEN I BOUGHT EVERYTHING IN SIGHT THAT CAME OUT FOR A ROLEPLAYING GAME, REGARDLESS. THOSE WERE DIFFERENT GAMES, DIFFERENT SYSTEMS. THAT WAS A DIFFERENT SITUATION ENTIRELY!

THAT WAS A DIFFERENT PERSON.

THAT WAS LAST WEEK.

O, BITTER FOLLY OF YOUTH!

56

DORK TOWER

BY JOHN KOVALIC

DORK TOWER

BY JOHN KOVALIC

OK, MAXWELL, CLOSING TIME. TIME TO GO.

TIME TO GO?

AAAIEEE! IT CAN'T BE! YOU CAN'T THROW ME OUT! HOW COULD YOU **DO** SUCH A THING?

DON'T YOU REALIZE THAT A GAME STORE IS SO MUCH **MORE** TO ROLE PLAYERS THAN JUST ANOTHER SHOP? IT'S OUR **REFUGE!**

THIS IS OUR **NIRVANA!** OUR **GATHERING PLACE!** WHERE WE MEET OUR FRIENDS! WHERE WE EXCHANGE **LAUGHS,** **IDEAS** AND **GOSSIP!** THIS IS WHERE WE CAN BE **OURSELVES!**

THIS ISN'T A **STORE.** IT'S A **SANCTUARY!**

I'M TOUCHED, MAXWELL.

THANK YOU.

BUT YOU'VE BEEN HERE FOR THREE WEEKS NOW ...

IF THIS IS ABOUT THE **CAMPFIRE** IN THE **COLLECTIBLE CARD** SECTION, I CAN DOUSE IT...

DORK TOWER

BY JOHN KOVALIC

WHAT'S NEW?
1 of 2
$5.95
Palliard Press
by Phil Foglio

CHAOTICALLY NEUTRAL HUMOR!

WHAT'S THIS, BILL?

OUR NEW GAMING TABLE!

NOW THE STORE **FINALLY** HAS AN AREA WHERE GAMERS CAN GATHER!

IMAGINE! WE'LL BE ABLE TO SPONSOR CONTESTS! EVENTS! **IN-STORE GAMING!**

WE'LL GET CARD GAMERS AND ROLE PLAYERS AND BOARD-GAMERS AND MINIATURE GAMERS COMING TO THE STORE FROM **ALL OVER THE CITY!**

PEGASAURUS GAMES

SOON NOW, PEGASAURUS GAMES WILL **RING** WITH THE SOUNDS OF **EPIC BATTLES** AND **MIGHTY CLASHES!**

BETWEEN WHO?

CARD GAMERS AND ROLEPLAYERS AND BOARDGAMERS AND MINIATURES GAMERS. THEY CAN'T STAND EACH OTHER... I'M THINKING OF CHARGING THE PUBLIC TO WATCH...

DORK TOWER

BY JOHN KOVALIC

LOSER
DORK! FREAK!

:SIGH: MORE ROLEPLAYERS AND CARD GAMERS BICKERING?

I'M **SICK** OF DIVISIVENESS IN GAMING! I'M GOING TO UNITE THESE FACTIONS IF IT'S THE **LAST** THING I DO!

ROLEPLAYERS! BACK OFF THE CARD GAMERS! BOARDGAMERS! STOP MOCKING THE ROLEPLAYERS! HISTORICAL BUFFS! FANTASY GAMING **ISN'T** THE END OF THE WORLD!

WE'RE ALL ONE HOBBY HERE, PEOPLE! CAN'T WE ALL JUST GET ALONG? ROLEPLAYERS, CARDGAMERS, BOARD GAMERS, MINIATURE ENTHUSIASTS **UNITE!**

LOOK AT ME! I'M A ROLEPLAYER **AND** A HISTORICAL WARGAMER **AND** A CARD FANATIC **AND** A BOARD GAMER!

:GASP: :OH: HE LIKES COLLECTIBLE CARD GAMES... AND ROLEPLAYING... AND BOARD GAMES... AND MINIS...

GET HIM!

LOSER! DORK! FREAK!

BY GOLLY, IT WORKED...

DORK TOWER

BY JOHN KOVALIC

STAR FLEET MISSION
A STAR FLEET UNIVERSE CARD GAME

HEY, IGOR! WANT TO SIGN UP FOR THE PEGASAURUS GAMES STORE SOFTBALL TEAM?

COOL!

BUT YOU KNOW... INSTEAD OF **THREE** OUTS PER INNING, WOULDN'T IT BE **FAR** MORE INTERESTING IF IT WAS A **RANDOM DIE ROLL** INSTEAD?

UH...

YES! AND THE PITCHER COULD ONLY THROW A FAST-BALL AFTER ROLLING **DOUBLES** ON 2D4, UNLESS IT WAS AFTER A **PREDETERMINED** MYSTERY INNING!

ERR...

THEN YOU ADD A **SPECIAL ABILITIES DECK!** OR A **RANDOM EFFECTS DECK!** OR A **DECK OF MANY THINGS!** YES! THE INFIELDERS GET RANDOM SELECTIONS OF **FARM IMPLEMENTS!**

NOW, THAT'S NOT...

OK! INSTEAD OF **THAT**, WHY NOT HAVE A **REFFEREE** WHO'S RESPONSIBLE FOR **HIDDEN TRAPS** THAT CAN BE SET BEFORE THE GAME? THAT OR SPECIAL ABILITIES!

OOO! OOO! OOOO! GREAT! SO WE **KEEP** THE 1D6 OUTS PER INNING, **DITCH** THE FARM IMPLEMENTS, AND COME UP WITH A **RANDOM OUTFIELDER ENCOUNTER TABLE!**

THE GAME OF **SOFTBALL** IS **NOT** OPEN TO **HOUSE RULES!**

THERE'S A **REASON** ROLEPLAYERS SELDOM MAKE THE WORLD SERIES, YOU REALIZE...

OK... NOW LET'S SAY THIRD BASE REPRESENTS A **WARP** PORTAL...

DORK TOWER

BY JOHN KOVALIC

WOO-HOO! STACY! LOOK AT THIS!

WHAT?

A FIGHTER I PAINTED UP FOR SATURDAY'S ROLEPLAYING GAME.

AH...

OK... LOOK CLOSELY... SQUINT... COUNT TO TEN, THEN GO "OOOO, NIIIICE"...

OOOO, NIIIICE..

WHAT A GREAT...

THEY'RE "MINIATURE FIGURES," NOT "LITTLE PEOPLE." THEY'RE "MINIATURE FIGURES," NOT "LITTLE PEOPLE."

...MINIATURE FIGURE. THE...

WHAT'S IT CALLED? WHAT'S IT CALLED? WHAT'S IT CALLED?

...DRYBRUSHING IS LOVELY.

NICE WORK, SWEETIE! NIIICE WORK!

THANKS, HON!

DATING A GAMER. IT'S NOT JUST A JOB: IT'S AN ART FORM.

OK... NOW SIT DOWN. I WANT TO TELL YOU ABOUT MY ELVEN MAGE/THIEF FOR THE NEXT HALF-HOUR...

DORK TOWER

BY JOHN KOVALIC

FRANK, YOU'RE DEAD.

LORY, YOU'RE DEAD.

SCOTT, YOU'RE DEAD. NEXT TURN

PEGASAURUS GAMES
OPEN

HI, BILL. UH...WHAT'S GOING ON?

THAT? THAT'S JUST THE **IN-STORE GAMING** GROUP.

RANDY, YOU'RE DEAD.

TERRY, YOU'RE DEAD.

NEXT TURN.

AS PART OF ITS **SILVER ANNIVERSARY**, TSR RELEASED SOME OF ITS **CLASSIC** DUNGEONS AND DRAGONS ADVENTURES, IT'S GIVEN GAMERS **EVERYWHERE** A CHANCE TO RE-EXPERIENCE THEM!

JIM, YOU'RE DEAD,

KARL, YOU'RE DEAD

KATZ, YOU'RE DEAD.

NEXT TURN.

SO TO **JOIN IN** THE CELEBRATION, THE GROUP IS WORKING ITS WAY THROUGH SOME OF THE MOST **HALLOWED** ADVENTURES IN GAMING **HISTORY!**

BOTH BILLS ARE DEAD.

PAUL, LIZ AND CARSON ARE DEAD.

SCOTT'S DEAD. AGAIN. NEXT TURN.

WOW.

DAVE, YOU'RE DEAD.

LARRY, YOU'RE DEAD.

AARON, YOU'RE DEAD.

AND SO'S YOUR DOG.

TODAY, OF COURSE, IT'S "THE TOMB OF HORRORS."

OK. EVERYBODY ROLL UP ANOTHER CHARACTER. DONE? GOOD. THEY'RE DEAD, TOO...

64

DORK TOWER BY JOHN KOVALIC

What's new, big Cliff o comic store manager?

"Danger Chix"

"Danger Chix?"

Oh, yes.

WEST CAPITAL COMICS

It's perpetually late, sometimes months so, and its many, many, **MANY** variant covers seem intended to court the speculator market rather than the average comics fan.

And it'd be nice to see the energy that goes into "Danger Chix" marketing, Hollywood rights and collectible toys go into the comics themselves, since the plots — such as they are — are pretty flimsy.

Most involve simplistic cases that they solve.

..half-naked...

I'll take — I say — I'll take a dozen!

65

DORK TOWER BY JOHN KOVALIC

WHY ARE YOU SUCH A HUGE COMICS FAN, IGOR?

OOOOOO. LOTS OF REASONS.

BUT MOSTLY, I THINK IT'S THAT COMICS ARE A **UNIQUE** ART FORM. NO OTHER MEDIA IS QUITE LIKE IT AT ALL!

IMAGINE YOU PUT OUT A COMIC BOOK: YOU HAVE **PAGE** AFTER **PAGE** TO TELL **ANY** STORY YOU WANT TO. YOU CAN CREATE **BOLD** NEW UNIVERSES.

YOUR ONLY LIMIT IS YOUR VISION AND IMAGINATION.

THINK WHAT YOU COULD COME UP WITH! **DARE TO DREAM** WHAT ORIGINAL CREATIONS YOU COULD FORGE! **NO** BOUNDRIES OR LIMITS! JUST **BRAVE NEW VISTAS!**

COMICS CAN TAKE YOU TO WORLDS **NO** OTHER MEDIA **CAN!**

SO WHAT ARE YOU PICKING UP?

"TOMB RAIDER," "STAR WARS" AND "CLERKS." OOOO! LOOK! THERE'S ALSO A NEW "BUFFY THE VAMPIRE SLAYER" OUT!

DORK TOWER BY JOHN KOVALIC

WHAT'S THAT, IGOR?

≥GASP≤ IT'S THIS MONTH'S HOT COMIC!

HUZZAH! I'VE READ SO MUCH ABOUT THIS COMIC BOOK, THIS WORK OF ART, THIS SHINY, NEW MASTERPIECE... IT MUST BE MINE!

ALL THE ANTICIPATION... ALL THE PREVIEWS... ALL THE HYPE AND WAIT... IT'S NOT JUST A COMIC, IT'S A PUBLISHING EVENT OF THE UTMOST IMPORTANCE!

OH.

THIS IS A COMIC BOOK FOR THE AGES! A SOARING WORK OF SEQUENTIAL ART THAT WILL MAKE LIFE ITSELF WORTH LIVING! THIS IS A COMIC BOOK THAT WILL NEVER BE FORGOTTEN!

I SEE.

AND WHAT'S THIS IN THE $.25 BIN?

LAST MONTH'S HOT COMIC. WHY DO YOU ASK?

DORK TOWER
BY JOHN KOVALIC

NEW COMIC OUT?

ISSUE #1 OF LADY BADGIRL! IT'S JUST IN!

;‡ ... BUT LADY BADGIRL ISN'T A **NEW** COMIC!

OH, NO. THE COMPANY JUST STARTED NUMBERING THEM FROM #1 AGAIN.

SOUNDS LIKE A **CYNICAL** MARKETING PLOY.

AU CONTRAIRE! IT'S A WAY TO REVIVE INTEREST IN A COMIC THAT'S SALES ARE TANKING, PERHAPS, BUT IT'S **SO** MUCH MORE!

RELAUNCHING A TITLE FROM #1 IS A WAY TO PUMP SOME **CREATIVE ENERGY** INTO A ONCE-VITAL COMIC, ALLOWING FANS AND COLLECTORS TO APPRECIATE THE **VIBRANCE** AND **VIGOR** OF SEQUENTIAL ART AT ITS FINEST! **YOW!**

FASCINATING.

YUP.

HOW MANY ISSUES HAD IT GOTTEN **UP** TO?

TWO. OOOO! IT'S RELAUNCHING AS #1 AGAIN **NEXT** MONTH! PULL-LIST CITY!

DORK TOWER
BY John Kovalic

...JUST AS THE GIANT AURORIAN BATTLE BUDGIE REACHES YOU, SIR BALDWIN, YOU REALIZE THAT THE ROOM YOU FLED TO IS NOTHING MORE THAN THE OLD "BLOCK OF GRANITE TO THE HEAD" TRAP...

≈ULP≈

BETWEEN THE BLOCK, THE BUDGIE AND THE FIFTEEN FUMBLED SAVING ROLLS, I'M AFRAID SIR BALDWIN HAS... UH... BEEN KILLED, IGOR.

WHAT?

DEAD? BALDWIN IS DEAD? DEAD?

NOW, TRY NOT TO GET TOO UPSET ABOUT...

DEAD?

DEAD! DEAD! DEAD! YES! YES! YES!

HA HA HA HA HA! WOOO-WOOOO! YES! YES! YES! YEEESS!

HIS BRAIN WAS MASHED-IT WAS A MONSTER MASH! HIS LIFE WAS SNATCHED! OH IT WAS REALLY SCRATCHED!

HIS SPINE WAS SMASHED! HE'S IN A GRAVEYARD, NATCH! HA HA HA HA! YESSSSS! SEE YA, LOOOOSER!

THE GRIM REAPER KINDA LOSES HIS STING WHEN HE CLAIMS A LOW-STAT CHARACTER YOU'VE BEEN STUCK WITH, DOESN'T HE..?

OK. DONE WITH THE GRIEVING PROCESS. GOT TO ROLL UP A NEW CHARACTER.

WHAT A PITY!

DORK TOWER
By JOHN KOVALIC

WHOAH! IT'S IN! THE DANGER CHIX **GOLD FOIL VARIANT COVER!**

GOLD FOIL VAR...

AIEEE! CAREFUL! THAT'S THE **RAREST** OF **ALL** THE VARIANT COVERS!

"...ALL OF THE...?

ALL OF THEM! FROM THE **NAUGHTY NIGHTY NATASHA** COVER TO THE **SILVER STAMPED SWIM-SUIT** COVER!

THE **HOLOGRAPHIC** TUSHIE COVER WAS, OF COURSE, A CLASSIC... AS WAS THE BOMBASTIC "BIRTHDAY SUIT" COVER, THE PERVY ALTERNATIVE ILLUSTRATOR COVER AND THE R-RATED "**WONDERWHIP**" COVER.

WOW.

THIS COMIC HAS GIVEN ITS FANS DOZENS OF EXCITING, AMAZING, HOT **VARIANT COVERS** TO **COLLECT** AND **COVET!**

ONE DAY THEY MAY EVEN GIVE US ANOTHER **ISSUE**...

KOVALIC © 1998 SHETLAND PRODUCTIONS

DORK TOWER

BY JOHN KOVALIC

YOU GOING ONLINE AGAIN, IGOR?

OH, YES.

TYPE TYPE TYPE

IT'S KIND OF A HOME AWAY FROM HOME, A GATHERING OF LIKE-MINDED INDIVIDUALS THE **WORLD** OVER.

TYPE TAP TAPPA TYPE

IT'S A LINK - NAY - A **LIFELINE** BETWEEN COMIC BOOK FANBOYS, TREKKERS AND GAMERS THAT CROSSES **ENTIRE CONTINENTS**.

TYPE TYPE TAP TYPE

THE NET'S REVITALIZED LETTER WRITING, CREATED NEW COMMUNITIES AND **UNIFIED** FANDOM!

TYPE TAP TAPPITY TAP TAP

REALLY?

REALLY. ALL WE HAVE TO DO IS **POST** SOMETHING, SAY, ON SOME GENERAL COMIC BOOK TOPIC...

≥CLICK≤

AND **WAIT**...

≥DING≤ YOU'VE GOT MAIL.

DEAR NAZI REACTIONARY LOSER SCUMBAG...

AND THERE I WAS, STUCK IN THE LAST CENTURY...

DORK TOWER BY JOHN KOVALIC

OH MY GOD! THEY KILLED MEGA-DUDE!

THE COMICS COMPANY KILLED OFF THE MOST POPULAR CHARACTER IN THE **HISTORY** OF COMICS! THOSE **VISIGOTHS!** THOSE... THOSE...

OH... ₤PHEW₤ THEY BRING HIM BACK NEXT ISSUE.

IGOR! WELL, **DUH!**

X-MEN

DC

PUBLISHERS KILL OFF AND RESURRECT SUPERHEROES FASTER THAN YOU CAN SAY "AUNT MAY"! ALL IT TAKES IS DECLINING SALES! IT'S MEDIA MANIPULATION! DID ANYONE **REALLY** BELIEVE SUPER-MAN WAS DEAD, OR BAT-MAN'S BACK WAS BROKEN FOR GOOD? EVERYTHING'S BACK TO NORMAL SOON ENOUGH, BUT PEOPLE **STILL** BELIEVE THE HYPE!

₤GASP₤ YOU'RE **RIGHT!**

ONE DAY, FANS WILL **STOP** BUYING INTO THE CORPORATE GAMES THESE **GREEDHEADS** PLAY. **ONE DAY**, REPORTERS AND COLUMNISTS WILL REALIZE THEY'RE BEING **HAD!**

YES! YES, BY GOLLY, **YES!**

AND YOU KNOW, I THINK THAT DAY IS COMING **SOONER** RATHER THAN...

OH MY GOD! THEY KILLED MEGA-DUDE **AGAIN!**

HUZZAH! THE LAST "JAY AND SILENT BOB" IS FINALLY OUT!

GAAH!

"GAAH"?

GAAH. LOOK, AM I THE ONLY PERSON WHO'S A LITTLE SICK AND TIRED OF KEVIN SMITH?

I MEAN, THE MAN IS FREAKING EVERYWHERE! ACTING, DIRECTING, WRITING, PUMPING OUT ALTERNATIVE COMICS, MAINSTREAM COMICS, ACTION FIGURES... HE EVEN OWNS A COMIC STORE, FOR GOODNESS' SAKES!

GIVE IT A REST! ENOUGH ALREADY! CAN WE SAY "OVERKILL"? SO MISTER PROFESSIONAL FANBOY MADE GOOD! ARE THERE NO OTHER CREATORS IN THE COMICS FIELD THESE DAYS? DOES EVERYTHING DEEMED "KEWL" HAVE TO BE SOMETHING KEVIN BLEEDING SMITH SANCTIFIED?

WELL WHOOP-DE-FREAKING-DOO! IF HE WAS STANDING RIGHT HERE IN FRONT OF ME, YOU KNOW WHAT I'D SAY TO HIM? YOU KNOW WHAT I'D SAY?

"I DESPERATELY WANT TO BE YOU"?

NO. AFTER THAT...

DORK TOWER

BY JOHN KOVALIC

WHOAH. THIS TSR **SILVER ANNIVERSARY** REALLY TAKES ME BACK.

OH, THE MEMORIES. WHAT A TIME: THE **EARLIEST** DAYS OF **ADVENTURE GAMING!** THE **BIRTH** OF **ROLE PLAYING!**

IT WAS A **MAGIC** TIME, FULL OF LIVING **LEGENDS** AND INDUSTRY **GIANTS!** IT WAS **INTOXICATING!**

IT WAS A TIME OF **BREATHLESS ANTICIPATION:** EACH NEW RELEASE SEEMED **GROUNDBREAKING** EACH NEW MODULE WAS **REVOLUTIONARY!**

AHHHH, YES. WHEN FOLKS TALK WITH **WONDER** OF THE DIM, SHADOWY **PREHISTORY** OF OUR HOBBY, I CAN SAY **I** WAS **THERE!**

THE RELEASE OF **SECOND EDITION** ADVANCED DUNGEONS AND DRAGONS?

DUDE! NO WAY! HE'S GOT TO BE TALKING ABOUT **MAGIC: THE GATHERING ANTIQUITIES!**

IF ANYBODY NEEDS ME, I'LL BE IN THE STOCK ROOM FEELING OLD. VERY, **VERY** OLD...

DUDE—THERE WAS LIFE BEFORE PLANESCAPE? GET **OUT** OF HERE!

"Americans should know the universe itself as a road, as many roads, as roads for traveling souls."

- *Walt Whitman*

"What's that say kids? Walley World next three exits."

- *Clark Griswold,*
National Lampoon's Vacation

The road goes ever on and on...
The Lord of the Rings, JRR Tolkien

82

THAT AFTERNOON...

OK... WHAT'S LEFT TO DO ...?

≳GROAN≲

Panel 2:

MATT- YOU LOOK BEAT!

OH, I'M JUST EXHAUSTED.

LOOK AT THIS LIST! I'VE GOT TO BAG, GRADE AND BOX **ALL** THE COMICS I BOUGHT OVER THE LAST THREE MONTHS ... I HAVE TO CLEAN OUT **FOUR** CLOSETS TO MAKE ROOM FOR ALL MY GAMES THAT DON'T FIT ELSE-WHERE ... I HAVE TO FINISH A DUNGEON ADVENTURE BY **MONDAY** AND A DISPLAY CABINET FOR EIGHTY-FIVE ACTION FIGURES **ASAP** ... I HAVE TO SORT OUT MY SCHEDULE SO I CAN GET TO **TWO** CONVENTIONS THIS MONTH ...

THERE'S **SO** MUCH TO GET **DONE!**

Panel 3:

MAN.

Panel 4:

I NEED A **HOBBY.**

I MEAN, **LOOK** AT ALL THE UNPAINTED MINIATURES I'VE GOT!

THERE ARE HUNDREDS OF THEM! MAYBE **THOUSANDS**! I'LL **NEVER** GET TIME TO PAINT THEM ALL! NEVER! ALL IT DOES IS **DEPRESS** ME THAT I'VE SO MANY LEFT TO GET TO, SO I END UP LOOKING FOR SOMETHING TO DO TO MAKE ME **HAPPY**!

AND WHAT MAKES YOU HAPPY?

BUYING MORE MINIATURES ...

WHY DON'T YOU JUST CUT BACK ON NEW GAMES, THEN?

ARE YOU **INSANE**?

7th CHEESE

I'VE **GOT** TO KEEP UP ON ALL THE HOT NEW GAMES! I NEED TO KNOW WHAT'S STATE OF THE ART! I HAVE TO SPEND **HOURS** DEVOURING THEM OR RISK GETTING LEFT BEHIND!

THEN I CAN GO INTO THE GAMES STORE OR GO ONLINE AND SPEND HOURS **MORE** DISCUSSING, DEBATING AND DECONSTRUCTING EACH, CONTRASTING AND COMPARING, ALL IN INTELLECTUAL GIVE-AND-TAKE OF THE **GRANDEST ORDER**!

SO WHEN DO YOU ACTUALLY GET TIME TO PLAY THEM?

$%* ... **PLAY** THEM?

MAN, I NEED TO GET AWAY FROM IT ALL.

I NEED TO TAKE A BREAK. I NEED A VACATION. I NEED A CHANGE OF SCENE ... SOMETHING WILDLY DIFFERENT! I NEED TO TRAVEL SOMEWHERE AND GET SOMEPLACE WHERE I CAN FIND NEW SIGHTS, NEW SOUNDS AND COMPLETELY NEW EXPERIENCES!

... WITH A GOOD GAMES STORE NEARBY...

YOU ALSO NEED HELP ...

WELL, THERE'S ALWAYS BIG CON™...

BIG CON™? ARE YOU CRAZY, IGOR? WE COULDN'T POSSIBLY MAKE IT TO BIG CON™!

WHY NOT?

KEN CAN'T GO. HE'S ON A BUSINESS TRIP

YUP

CARSON CAN'T GO. HE'S JUST STARTED HIS JOB.

RIGHT.

IT'S HALF THE COUNTRY AWAY AND WE HAVE NO CAR.

TRUE.

WE DON'T HAVE THE TIME AND WE DON'T HAVE THE MONEY.

UH-HUH.

AND IT ALREADY STARTED. WE'D ONLY MAKE THE LAST DAY...

YUPPERS.

WAY KEWL! IN **FACT**, I WAS JUST TELLING GILLY...

WHO'S GILLY?

OH, JUST THIS FRIEND OF MINE FROM THE "MUD BAY BY NIGHT" GROUP...

:GROAN: GOTHS.

NO, NO, NO! SHE'S GREAT! I THINK YOU'D REALLY LIKE HER...

IN **FACT**, YOU KNOW, I DON'T KNOW WHY I DIDN'T THINK OF THIS BEFORE, BUT YOU TWO WOULD MAKE A GREAT...

AIEEE! LOOK OUT! RABBIT! SCREEEEEEEE!

PUFF WHEEZE PUFF PUFF

HOP HOP HOP

WHEW

NOW, WHAT WERE YOU SAYING?

HMM? OH, I FORGET. **HEY!** A GAMES, SF MEMORABILIA AND COMICS SHOP! **STOP!**

88

HITTING THE HARD STUFF ALREADY, CARSON?

WELL, IT'S **NOT** TURNING OUT TO BE ONE OF MY BETTER DAYS.

IGOR AND MATT...

MATT?

A FRIEND OF OURS, ANYWAY, **THEY'RE** OFF TO BIG CON™, AND I'M STUCK HERE.

AND TO MAKE MATTERS **WORSE**, THE **OTHER** MEMBER OF OUR GAMING GROUP IS ON A **BUSINESS TRIP**, SO THERE'S **NOBODY** TO GAME WITH HERE ANYWAY!

...TO SAY NOTHING OF THE FACT THAT I SEEM TO HAVE MISPLACED THE RENT MONEY. AND THE CAR...

OH, CARSON, YOU SILLY! DON'T THINK ABOUT IGOR! DON'T THINK ABOUT HIM AT **ALL**!

JUST THINK OF ALL THAT **FREE TIME** YOU HAVE NOW! THINK OF ITS **POTENTIAL**! THINK WHAT YOU COULD **DO** WITH IT!

UMMMMM...

"WHO WANTS TO SURVIVE MARRYING A BIG BROTHER'S MILLIONAIRE" IS ON TONIGHT...

SO **WHERE** DID YOU SAY IGOR IS NOW ...?

91

SOMETIME IN SOUTHERN ILLINOIS.

SLEEP DEPRIVATION... EXHAUSTION ...THE PLAINS STATES... WHAT CAN WE DO TO KEEP AWAKE?

I'VE GOT IT!

TRAVEL GAMES! WE PLAYED THEM ALL THE TIME WHEN I WAS A KID! LIKE LICENSE PLATE BINGO!

OF COURSE, IT COULD USE SOME HOUSE RULES ...

ONE HOUR LATER ...OR A MARMOT. WHICH IS WHY ROCK/PAPER/SCISSORS SHALL BE USED IN THE EVENT OF A TIE. NOW, RULE 31 B...

ONE HOUR LATER ...AND ALSO TO CARS FROM CANADA, MEXICO OR IOWA. SUB-SECTION SIX: WHAT TO DO IN CASE OF FOG, HAILSTORMS OR PAUL HARVEY ...

ONE HOUR LATER ...NOT, OF COURSE, CONFLICTING WITH RULE 126 B, PARAGRAPH TWO, UNDER THE HEADING "STUCKEYS."

I THINK WE CAN ALL AGREE ON THAT...

ONE HOUR LATER ...EXCEPT IN CASES OF SUBARUS!

(I CAN'T BELIEVE THEY RAN OUT OF X-MEN HAPPY MEALS HERE...)

RULE 312 ...

ONE HOUR LATER ...AND TWO DAVENPORTS! RIGHT. I THINK THAT'S EVERYTHING!

OK. SO, THOSE ARE THE BASIC RULES. NOW FOR ADVANCED AND OPTIONAL RULES ...

DUDE! OHMIGOSH! WE'RE HERE!

BIGCON!™ THE GRANDADDY OF ALL CONVENTIONS!

BIGCON!™ EVEN ON ITS LAST DAY, IT'S A THING OF WONDER TO BEHOLD!

BIGCON!™ AT LAST! A CHANCE FOR REST AND RELAXATION!

BUT FIRST, I NEED... I NEED...

92

I NEED A NEW JOB

SO THE BUSINESS TRIP'S NOT GOING WELL, KEN?

URGH! AWFUL. DON'T ASK. HOW'S EVERYTHING THERE?

OH, I'VE GOTTEN **NOTHING** ACCOMPLISHED AT ALL! YESTERDAY WAS A **COMPLETE** WRITE OFF.

I WANTED TO GET SO MUCH DONE. **BLEAH.**

"BLEAH?"

IT'S DISAPPOINTING. I THOUGHT I'D HAVE ACCOMPLISHED **SOMETHING** WITH THIS TIME TO MYSELF.

I COULD HAVE SPENT THE ENTIRE DAY IN BED, WATCHING GAME-SHOWS, AND HAVE GOTTEN MORE DONE.

BUT TODAY'S ANOTHER DAY! I'M GOING TO GET UP, MAKE A NEW START AND **SEIZE THE DAY!**

WHAT TIME IS IT THERE?

NOON. DO YOU HAVE A POINT?

OK, HEINRICH, SPIN THAT WHEEL!

CLK CLK CLK CLK CLK

BIG MONEY! BIG MONEY!

HMPHH. WELL, I SUPPOSE MATT AND IGOR SHOULD BE AT BIG CON™ SOON, AT LEAST.

ACTUALLY, I RECKON THEY SHOULD BE PULLING IN ABOUT NOW.

OF COURSE, THAT DOESN'T LEAVE THEM WITH A **LOT** OF TIME.

BUT STILL, **HALF** A DAY AT BIG CON™ IS BETTER THAN **NONE**...

DORK TOWER BY JOHN KOVALIC

WOO-HOO! IT'S **IN!**

"WARHAMSTER: SEVENTH BRAVE NEW HUNTER"! THE LATEST, NEWEST, COOLEST, MOST **PHAT** RPG EVER!

THIS GAME HAS **EVERYTHING!** ATTITUDE, BACKGROUND, FLY DEVELOPMENT, FRESH PRODUCTION VALUES! DUDE! JUST **LOOK** AT THOSE **FULL** COLOR PLATES!

AND THE GAME WORLD! THE RICH, RICH HISTORIES! THE NATION STATES! THE PERSONALITIES! THE ROOM FOR EXPANDING GEOPOLITICAL STORYLINES! THERE'S **NOTHING** THEY **FORGOT!**

RULES?

DAMN!

IGOR'S
BRIEF BUT HELPFUL
GUIDE TO
CONVENTION -GOING!

① PREPARE, PREPARE, PREPARE!

THERE'LL BE **PLENTY** OF TIME TO DO EVERY-THING I WANT TO...

...IF I JUST SKIP EATING... SLEEPING...

CONVENTION SCHEDULE

AIEEEEEEEE!

DUE TO SCHED CONFLICTS, CLAUDIA CHRISTIA WON'T EVEN BE IN THE SAME TIME ZONE AS YOU...

② THE GUEST WHO WAS YOUR MAIN REASON FOR TRAVELING TO THE CON IN THE FIRST PLACE **WILL** CANCEL AT THE LAST MINUTE.

③ HOWEVER, SUBSTITUTES WILL BE FOUND.

YOU'RE REALLY...UH... THE GUY WHO PLAYED THE THIRD EWOK FROM THE LEFT IN THAT SCENE THAT WAS CUT FROM "JEDI"?

NO FOOLIN'.

AUTOGRAPHS ARE $15.

④ THE HOT NEW PRODUCT YOU'RE SEARCHING FOR WILL BE SOLD OUT.

GRRRR

7TH CHEESE OUT OF STOCK!

LOSER!

⑤ BUT DON'T WORRY— THERE'LL BE **LOTS** OF OTHER STUFF TO BUY!

GRRRR

HOUSE OF POKÉMON

POKÉMON

MORE POKÉMON

LOOK IT! POKÉMON

⑥ ANYWAY, IT'S NOT LIKE YOU'LL HAVE ANY MONEY LEFT, ANYWAY!

THE GOLD FOIL VARIANT COVER "DANGER CHIX" #3? THAT'LL BE $42.76.

DANGER CHIX!

⑦ SO RELAX AND ENJOY! PUT YOUR FEET UP! HAVE A BITE TO EAT!

THE CHILI DOG? THAT'LL BE $42.76.

⑧ AND REMEMBER: THERE'LL BE **OTHER** CONVENTIONS!

AIEEE ETC...

DUE TO SCHEDULE CONFLICTS, JERI RYAN WANTS NOTHING TO DO WITH YOU LOSERS.

© 1999 SHETLAND PRODUCTIONS

JOHN KOVALIC

DORK TOWER ABROAD

DORK TOWER is translated into German, French, Italian and (by way of a certain pirate web site) Hungarian these days (and it looks like authorized Spanish and Portuguese translations are close at hand).

Some puns, of course, don't translate. "Dork Covenant," for example, will soon be called "World of Dumb People" in Germany. And the cover will also change, since few Germans would get the first edition Dungeons and Dragons Players Handbook parody artwork, according to my publisher there.

But mostly it does seem to cross overseas OK. The strip below, for example, is usually the first one to be requested by new publishers. Now you, too, can say "Hey, Marcia! Come and see the satanist" in five different languages!

DORK STORM

#11

$2.95

DORK TOWER

WORLD OF
DORKNESS

"Baby we're the same, when we shine in each other's eyes."

- *Matthew Sweet*

WORLD OF DORKNESS

SPLIK   SPLIK   SPLIK   SPLIK

"Loser" (Beck)©1993 Geffen Records

WHAT ARE YOU DOING HERE THIS LATE ANYWAY, IGOR?

OH, I JUST WANTED TO CHECK UP ON SOMETHING. WHAT'S IT LIKE HERE AT NIGHT?

ARE YOU **KIDDING?** I HATE THE LATE SHIFT! THIS IS WHEN THE **ANTSY** CROWD COMES OUT!

REALLY?

THE CHAT ROOM

REALLY! THE ARTSY GOTHS, THE AWFUL POETS, THE PRETENTIOUS POSERS, THE PSEUDO-INTELLECTUALS, THE AWKWARD FIRST DATES, THE UGLY LAST DATES, THE PHILOSOPHY STUDENTS, THE POST-SHOW PLAYGOERS, THE PRE-SHOW PUNKS, **YOU NAME IT!**

THE FREAKS, THE WEIRDOS, THE GEEKS...

THE **LOO-SERS.**

SAY, ISN'T THAT **MATT** OVER THERE...

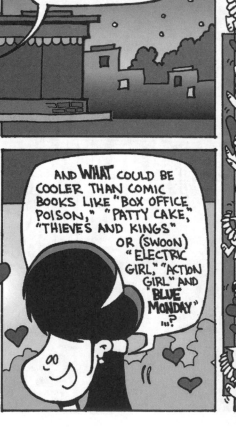

DORK TOWER BY JOHN KOVALIC

IN: THE COST OF LOAFING

HOW MUCH FOR THOSE GOURMET COOKIES?

$3 EACH

GREAT! A DOZEN, PLEASE.

MR COOKIE

THESE SNEAKERS, PLEASE.

$87.

OK.

ONE TICKET FOR "MYSTERY MEN."

$14

AND SOME POPCORN

MAKE IT $21.

HOW MUCH ARE NINTENDO GAMES NOW?

$75.

I'LL TAKE TWO.

MORTAL WOMBAT

CHRONIC THE HEDGEHOG

$29.95 FOR A ROLE PLAYING GAME? DO THESE COMPANIES' GREED KNOW NO ENDS?

HOLD ON. YOU LEFT YOUR $5 CUP OF COFFEE HERE...

WAR HAMSTER

DORK TOWER BY JOHN KOVALIC

OK GUYS... IT **FINALLY** CAME IN! **WARHAMSTER: GLORIANA!** ROLEPLAYING IN ELIZABETHAN ENGLAND!

SNIFF... I'M SO HAPPY...

IT'S GOT **EVERYTHING!** DEE-ESQUE HERMETIC LORE AND INTRICATE MEMORY PALACES! DRAMATURGICAL MAGICK, OCCULT IMPERIALISM, SEA DOGS AND THE SPANISH ARMADA! RELIGIOUS ESPIONAGE, MASQUES, SACRED GEOMETRY AND **NEO-CLASSICAL INVOCATIONS!**

IT'S SHAKESPEARE, BACON AND MOORE! DEMONOLOGY AND MURRAYESQUE AND JACOBEAN WITCHCRAFT! COURT INTRIGUE AND EARLY CRYPTOGRAPHY! TERRA INCOGNITO AND REVENGE DRAMA! PROSPERO AND **FAERIE WORLDS!**

ITS MERCENARY POLITICS AND SPENSERIAN IMAGERY AND LOST CITIES, PROTO-ROSICRUCIANISM AND **EVERYTHING!**

AND YOU CAN BASH THINGS IN—

HUZZAH! HURRAH! HEY, NONNY NONNY!

117

DORK TOWER
BY JOHN KOVALIC

WOO-HOO! THIS TIME I'VE **REALLY** DONE IT!

WHAT?

I'VE CREATED THE **ULTIMATE** STARTING CHARACTER USING WARHAMSTER'S SYSTEM OF COUNTERBALANCING **ADVANTAGES** AND DISADVANTAGES

OH.

THIS IS **INCREDIBLE**, BUT THE NUMBERS ADD UP! OF COURSE, I HAD TO TAKE SOME PRETTY SERIOUS DISADVANTAGES TO WORK THIS, BUT JUST **LISTEN** TO HIS ADVANTAGES!

NUMBER ONE: HE HAS SUPER STRENGTH. NUMBER TWO: HE HAS PHOTOGRAPHIC MEMORY. NUMBER THREE: HE **STARTS** AS A TENTH-LEVEL WIZARD. NUMBER FOUR: HE HAS **NO** FEAR!

HOLY COW...

THAT'S JUST THE START! I WAS **ALSO** ABLE TO SCROUNGE UP RAPID HEALING, NIGHT VISION, POWERFUL ALLIES, WEALTH AND AN ENTIRE **ENTOURAGE** FOR HIM!

HE'S GOT SEX APPEAL, OFF-THE-BOARD CHARISMA, LUCK, A BROTHER WHO'S KING, WISDOM, ACUTE HEARING **AND** (BY REALLY WORKING THE NUMBERS) A **SUPERINTELLIGENT** ANIMAL COMPANION, **MAUDE** THE **WONDER CAT!**

WOW.

AND HIS DISADVANTAGES?

NUMBER ONE: HE'S DEAD...

DORK TOWER BY JOHN KOVALIC

TYPE TYPE
TYPE TYPE
TYPE TYPE
TYPE TYPE

CLICK
? SEND ?

THERE! I JUST POSTED THE GREATEST MESSAGE IN THE HISTORY OF REC.FAN.CHATTER!

MAN, WILL PEOPLE BE IMPRESSED! AN ENTIRE MISSIVE ON ROLEPLAYING, GOD AND THE MEANING OF LIFE!

SO YOU DIDN'T NOTICE YOU MISTYPED "ROLEPLAYING" AS "ROLFPLYING", "GOD" AS "GUD" AND "MEANING OF LIFE" AS "MANNING OF LOFD"?

AIEEE

THE INFORMATION AGE: LETTING YOU LOOK LIKE TWICE THE IDIOT IN HALF THE TIME...

"AND HOW DID "HANKY-PANKY" BECOME "SPANKY-SPANKY"? AIEEEE!

DORK TOWER

BY JOHN KOVALIC

OH NO, CAPTAIN HONEY, MA'AM! WE'RE DOOMED! THE STAR MONSTER HAS GRABBED THE *KAGEMUSHA*!

OOO! OOO!

OOO! OOO!

{GROAN} ANIME AGAIN?

ENGAGE THE RETRO-ROCKETS, SUKI! IT COULD BE OUR ONLY HOPE!

HONESTLY! MOST OF IT IS SO CLICHED AND SO POORLY WRITTEN, IT'S ASTOUNDING IT HAS ANY FOLLOWING AT ALL, LET ALONE THE ONE IT DOES!

AT LAST! CHYANA AND KATCHOO, THE TWINS, USED THEIR HYPNO-TRANCE TO DEFEAT IT! HA HA!

I MEAN, LOOK AT IT! THE ANIMATION IS JUST AWFUL! SATURDAY MORNING CARTOONS ARE MORE PROFESSIONAL! AND THE PLOTS HAVE ALL THE SUBTLETY AND SOPHISTICATION OF SLUDGE. ALL THE CHARACTERS ARE TWO-DIMENSIONAL AT MOST!

I JUST DON'T SEE WHY IT'S SO POPULAR!

LET'S TAKE ALL OUR CLOTHES OFF, NOW...

YES, I DO...

OH! WHERE DID THESE NAUGHTY TENTACLES COME FROM...?

120

DORK TOWER

BY JOHN KOVALIC

KEN — YOU BOUGHT A DVD PLAYER?

IT'S AWESOME! I'M TAKING IT OUT AND SETTING IT UP NOW!

IT'S GOT FIVE-DVD CAPACITY, MULTI-ZONE CAPABILITIES, SEVEN-SPEED FAST-FORWARD AND REVERSE, **PLUS** IT'S GOT UNBELIEVABLE...

GASP

CAN IT BE?

MIGHT IT BE?

OH JOY!

UNBELIEVABLE ECSTASY!

UNKNOWABLE BLISS!

HAPPINESS OF HUNDRED LIFETIMES!

STYROFOAM PACKAGING !!!

THE PEWTER FUMES GET TO MINIATURES PLAYERS AFTER A WHILE, NO?

OK...THIS PIECE IS A WARHAMSTER 40K SPACE MARINE BASE ...THIS PIECE IS A CASTLE... AND THIS PIECE IS OBVIOUSLY THE MID-RIFF OF THE BATTLESTAR GALACTICA FOLLOWING THE BATTLE OF ALPHA CYGNUS...

DORK TOWER

BY JOHN KOVALIC

OK...THE PARTY ARRIVES AT THE CAVERN ENTRY WHERE YOU SPY...

...A TURBONIUM DRAGON!

BRAVE NEW WORLD GLORY DAYS
A BRAVE NEW WORLD SOURCEBOOK
BY MATT FORBECK

HUZZAH! WE ATTACK!

OK...

ROLL ROLL ROLL

IGOR, YOU'RE INSTANTLY INCINERATED BY ITS FIREBALL BREATH!

PEGASAURUS GAMES
OPEN

WHAT?

SHAKE SHAKE ROLL ROLL

PAINFULLY, I MIGHT ADD. CARSON, YOU FUMBLE YOUR SAVING ROLL. YOU'RE A GONER.

IN-STORE GAMING TODAY

BUT NOT BEFORE THE DRAGON DECIDES TO USE YOUR SPINE FOR SPAGHETTI. OUCH.

ROLL ROLL

DWEEZIL, YOU'RE NOW A WELCOME MAT FOR THE DRAGON'S LAIR. OR WHAT'S LEFT OF YOU IS.

SHAKE SHAKE SHAKE

MORTY, YOU ARE SO TOAST!

WHAT AN UGLY END... AN UGLY, HUMILIATING, SICKENING END, MORTY. YOU'LL NEVER PLAY THE VIOLIN AGAIN.

AND GILLY, YOU...

ROLL ROLL SHAKE ROLL

...MAKE AN INCREDIBLE SKILL ROLL, FLIP BACKWARDS, BOUNCE BACK BEHIND HIM, AND WITH A TRIPLE SPIN STAB AT HIS HEART AND... ROLL ROLL ...MAKE IT ON A CRITICAL HIT! IN AN EVIL CLOUD OF TURBONIUM, THE DRAGON EXPIRES!

NEVER GET INTO A GAME WHERE THE GM HAS THE HOTS FOR A PLAYER

WHILE YOU'RE LOOTING YOUR COMPANIONS' BODIES, WHY DON'T I JUST ROUND UP YOUR EXPERIENCE POINTS TO THE NEAREST 100,000...

DORK STORM

#12
$2.95

DORK TOWER

WARHAMSTER

"If birds start up, there are ambushers there. If the animals are frightened, there are attackers there."

- Sun Tzu, The Art of War

I MEAN, THAT WAS LIKE **TEN DOLLARS,** MAN! **THREE WEEKS** IT TOOK ME TO SAVE UP THAT ALLOWANCE! **THEN** THEY RELEASED THOSE **OTHER** BOOKS FOR IT, WHICH TOOK **ALL** MY LAWNMOWING MONEY!

AND **NOW** THEY PUT OUT WARHAMSTER IN **HARDCOVER?** I CAN'T PAY FOR ALL THIS! I EXPECT TO BE DATING **HEAVILY** SOON, FOR PETE'S SAKE!

AND IT'S NOT EVEN **COMPLETE! NEXT** MONTH THEY'RE PUTTING OUT THE **DUNGEON MAKER'S GUIDE!**

TO SAY **NOTHING** ABOUT THE **MONSTER TOME!**

DO THEY **THINK** WE'RE MADE OUT OF **MONEY?** DO THEY **THINK** WE WANT TO BUY THE SAME GAME **OVER** AND **OVER?**

DON'T THEY THINK ABOUT THE FANS?

COOL DOWN, MATT. THEY PROBABLY JUST HAD TO CLEAN UP ALL THOSE **TYPOS,** AND CORRECT THOSE HOLES IN THE **RULES.** AND NEVER FORGETTING THAT THE **ART** NEEDED IMPROVING, BADLY.

HMMM...

IT TAKES **TIME** TO GET THINGS RIGHT.

WELL, AS LONG AS THIS DOESN'T HAPPEN **AGAIN** ...

IF YOU'RE **GOING** TO MAKE IGOR FAINT, YOU COULD AT LEAST WARN PEOPLE IN HIS PATH...

JUST WAVE SOME MAGIC: ANTIQUITIES CARDS UNDER HIS NOSE. HE'LL BE OK...

...UNLIKE **WARHAMSTER.**

HOW COULD THEY **DO** THIS? SECOND EDITION WAS SO ELEGANT... SO PERFECT!

IT WAS THE **KING** OF GAMES! THE PINNACLE! THE TOPS! WE SHALL NEVER SEE ITS LIKE AGAIN...

WAFT WAFT WAFT

INSTEAD, WE HAVE THIS MONSTROSITY... THIS ABERRATION... THIS VILE, WRETCHED PIECE OF **REFUSE!**

I HAVEN'T HATED A GAME **THIS** MUCH SINCE... SINCE...

...SINCE SECOND EDITION REPLACED FIRST EDITION?

THERE'S A **REASON** MUSKRAT PIE IS POPULAR IN MICHIGAN, YOU KNOW...

NO... NO... CARSON'S RIGHT. THERE'S MORE TO THIS THAN SIMPLY HAVING TO BUY A NEW EDITION...

SOMETHING'S **WRONG** HERE...

IT'S TRUE, MATT. YOU RANT ALL THE **TIME!**

YOU'VE RANTED ABOUT COMIC BOOKS' COVERS, COLLECTIBLE CARD GAMES, GOTHS, GAMERS, MUNDANES, POKÉMON...

I DON'T THINK I **EVER** HEARD ANY- ONE RANT ABOUT THE LITTLE SISTERS OF MERCY BEFORE I MET YOU, YOU KNOW...

OPEN GAMING

BUT YOU'VE **NEVER** RANTED ABOUT (GASP) **WARHAMSTER**!

WHAT'S WRONG, MATT?

"THIRD EDITION."

FEH!

"FEH"?

IGOR. HAS IT **EVER** STRUCK YOU THAT **MOST** OF THE GAMES WE PLAY ARE 20 YEARS OLD **AT BEST**?

"WARHAMSTER," "TRAVAILLER," "BERPS," "DUNGEONS AND DRAGOONS"... IS **EVERYTHING** A RETREAD OF AN OLD EDITION ANYMORE?

SURE SOME NEW MECHANICS ARE COOL, BUT WE'RE **STUCK IN THE PAST** JUST AS SURELY AS IF THIS WAS AN **OLDIES** RADIO STATION! WHERE'S THE **NEW WAVE?** WHERE'S THE **TRUE INNOVATION?**

FEH.

LET'S JUST SEE A MOVIE.

CHARLIE'S ANGELS?

I'LL GET MY COAT...

I MEAN, IS **THIS** HOW IT'S GOING TO BE FOREVER? WILL I **NEVER** BREAK OUT OF THIS **RUT?** WILL THAT **SPARK** THAT COULD CHANGE MY LIFE **ALWAYS** JUST **ELUDE** ME?

HEY, GILLY!

HEY, IGOR!

DO YOU **MIND?** I **AM** TRYING TO BARE MY SOUL HERE!

SORRY. SORRY. CARRY ON. YOU WERE SAYING..?

I'VE MEASURED OUT MY LIFE IN COFFEE SHOPS AND COMIC STORES, IGOR! CAN I EVEN TAKE A CHANCE ANY MORE? DO I **DARE** EAT A PEACH-FLAVORED **GUMMI** WORM?

LIFE'S SHORT! THIS ISN'T A DRESS REHEARSAL! **SOMETHING** HAS TO **CHANGE** HERE!

SO WHAT DO YOU DO ABOUT IT?

132

WHAT? WHAT?

ISN'T IT OBVIOUS, MATT? YOU'VE BECOME **ANOTHER** SAD CREATOR WRITING ABOUT THE KIND OF WOMAN YOU COULDN'T **BUY** A DATE WITH IN A MILLION YEARS...

I'M SORRY. I MEAN A CUTTING-EDGE ARTIST WHO'S CREATED AN ICONOCLASTIC CHARACTER THE LIKES OF WHICH THE INDUSTRY HAS NEVER, **EVER** KNOWN...

THANK YOU...

"THAT GRRRL" IS A MANIFESTATION OF MY **WORLD VIEW**! IT'S MY **PSYCHE** SPEAKING TO THE **MUSE** OF **CREATION**!

IT DOESN'T MEAN I HAVE THE **HOTS** FOR HER!

FOR GOODNESS SAKES, SHE'S **JUST** A CARTOON!

HONESTLY, IGOR! LISTENING TO YOU, ANYONE WOULD THINK COMIC BOOK ARTISTS WERE JUST DATELESS **DWEEBS** WITH A FETISH FOR **SPANDEX JUMPSUITS**!

SPANDEX JUMPSUITS.

SWEET, SWEET SPANDEX JUMPSUITS...

WELL, AS LONG AS MY MIND'S AT REST...

WAIT! HEAR ME OUT! MAYBE **SOME** CARTOONISTS FALL IN LOVE WITH THEIR SUPERHEROINES, BUT THAT'S TO BE **EXPECTED!**

IT IS?

SURE! ANYTHING YOU CREATE IS GOING TO BE A REFLECTION OF YOUR PERSONALITY TO **SOME** EXTENT!

WHAT'S WRONG WITH **THAT?**

IT'S **NOT** LUSTING AFTER FICTIONAL MEMBERS OF THE OPPOSITE SEX! IT'S JUST A **HEALTHY** PART OF THE **ARTISTIC** PROCESS!

SO THE COMIC **I'M** TRYING TO WRITE IS...?

PART OF **YOU!** IT'S AN EXPRESSION OF YOUR BELIEFS! OF YOUR **VERY** SOUL!

YOUR WORK IS YOU! YOUR CHARACTERS ARE YOU! YOUR **COMIC** IS YOU!

WHAT'S IT CALLED?

"DARKLADY VOLUPTRIX AND BREASTCHYLDE." CAN WE TALK ABOUT SOMETHING ELSE?

LIKE THE FACT THAT ANYBODY WHO WANTS TO START A COMIC BOOK THESE DAYS IS ALMOST CERTAINLY CERTIFIABLY INSANE!

HENCE "DARK-LADY VOLUPTRIX"?

HEY!

WHY DO YOU WANT TO MAKE A COMIC BOOK ANYWAY?

OH, I DON'T KNOW...

I SUPPOSE THE FEAR OF NOT TAKING A RISK IS GREATER THAN THE FEAR OF FAILURE! I DON'T WANT TO GET TO THE END OF MY LIFE NEVER HAVING TRIED TO FOLLOW A DREAM.

BUT I DON'T JUST WANT TO TAKE A RISK, I WANT TO MAKE A DIFFERENCE!

I DON'T KNOW EXACTLY WHAT IT IS I WANT TO SAY, BUT I KNOW I HAVE TO SAY SOMETHING, AND I HAVE TO DISCOVER THIS INSIDE ME!

IT'S LIKE A FIRE... ITS SOMETHING I CAN'T IGNORE!

I WANT TO FORGE IN THE SMITHY OF MY SOUL THE UNCREATED CONSCIENCE OF MY LIFE!

WHY DO YOU WANT TO MAKE A COMIC BOOK?

I WANT TO DRAW NAKED WOMEN. I...

THANK YOU ONCE AGAIN, MR. MENTAL IMAGE...

138

LOOK, IGOR, THIS IS MY CHANCE TO MAKE A **STATEMENT** HERE! TO PUT MY MONEY WHERE MY MOUTH IS, AND TO PUT MY IDEAS ON PAPER! I CAN CREATE A COMIC BOOK THAT HAS **HEART** AND **SOUL** AND **SPIRIT!** JUST **THINK** WHAT IT CAN TOUCH ON!

HMMMM...

AS LONG AS YOU AVOID GAMING HUMOR. GAMING HUMOR IS THE WORST.

WELL, DUH!

AND WHO **CARES** IF IT'S OBVIOUS I'M WRITING ABOUT A WOMAN OF MY **DREAMS?**

WRITING IS **ABOUT** DREAMS. **DRAWING** IS **ABOUT** DREAMS!

LIFE IS **ABOUT DREAMS!**

IT'S ABOUT DREAMING THAT THERE CAN BE SOMETHING **MORE** OUT THERE ...

IT'S ABOUT DREAMING THAT THE PERFECT WOMAN FOR YOU **IS** OUT THERE, EVEN THOUGH YOU **KNOW** IT'S JUST A DREAM.

...EVEN IF YOU KNOW SHE DOESN'T EXIST.

WELL DUH...

THAT GRRRL BY MATT McLIMORE

THE END!

139

DORK TOWER: The SHOPKEEP Files
BY JOHN KOVALIC

ONE FINE DAY AT THE COMICS STORE...

You know, I bet GAMES are where it's at...

SELLING COMIC BOOKS... SCRAPING BY EVERY MONTH... IT'S A TOUGH LIVING.

WORST EPISODE EVER

THE MARKET FLUCTUATIONS, THE INDUSTRY INCONSISTENCIES, THE UNCERTAINTIES OF THE COMIC BOOK WORLD... IT ALL POINTS TO THE FACT THAT I SHOULD BE LOOKING TO EXPAND INTO ANOTHER MARKET...

...BUT GAMES! WOW! LOOK AT THE GLITZ! THE PACKAGING! THE PRICE-POINTS AND THE PIZZAZZ! YES! THAT'S IT!

GAMES ARE WHERE IT'S AT!

MEANWHILE, AT THE GAMES STORE...

You know, I bet COMICS ARE WHERE IT'S AT...

WHAT ARE YOU DOING, IGOR.

OH... JUST THINKING...

ABOUT WHAT?

THE FUTURE.

THE FUTURE?

THE FUTURE, FULL OF POTENTIAL! FULL OF PROMISE AND DELIRIOUS DREAMS.

A FUTURE THAT COULD ASCEND THE HIGHEST HEAVENS OF INVENTION A FUTURE FREE OF WANT AND FULL OF EXCITEMENT!

BUT ONE THAT'S TEMPERED BY UGLY ECONOMIC REALITIES, HUMAN FRAILTIES, LUST, AVARICE AND ENVIOUS DESIRE!

WOW.

THESE TIMES JUST GET ME THINKING ABOUT THAT.

OH, YES ...

CHRISTMAS DOES THAT TO A PERSON.

CHRISTMAS?

I WAS TALKING ABOUT A TRIP TO THE GAMES STORE ...

END

THE DORK TOWER FAMILY...

DORK TOWER runs three times a week at GameSpy.com and once a week at Pyramid Magazine (http://www.sjgames.com/pyramid) It also appears monthly in DRAGON MAGAZINE and SCRYE MAGAZINE. In Europe, it's published in VALKYRIE (UK), POWER KAOS (Italy), BACKSTAB (France) and RINGBOTE (Germany).

Its latest home is in the huge Ziff-Davis publication, INTERACTIVE WEEK (below). You can get a free subscription to this massive, fun mag by going to http://www.zdnet.com/zdsubs/. And of course, for all the latest Dorky Goodness, go to http://kovalic.com.

If you're lucky enough at GenCon or some other Summer show, you might catch TOON guru Doc Cross running THE DUNGEON OF ULTIMATE DOOM!

Even if you don't, here is his warped vision on the Dork Tower gang...the attribute/skill numbers in parentheses are for the characters the Dorks are playing. The usually lower numbers not in parentheses are for the Dorks themselves, should you want to play them straight.

MATT (Elrond Hubbard)

Race/Class: Half-Elf Scout   **Hit Points:** 9 (30)

Speed: 5 (6)

Muscle: 4 (5)   **Zip:** 4 (10)
Smarts: 5 (6)   **Chutzpah:** 4 (7)

Shticks: Know Obscure Fact: 7 (Incredible Luck: 8) (Set/Disarm Trap: 10)

Stuff: Bag of Humongous Holding, Thieves Tools, +4 Cloak of Hiding, +36 Daggers of Backstabbing (+3 to hit, 1D+3 damage, double damage for backstabs), +6 Boots of Hauling Butt (gives +6 to Speed IF you are running from danger. Lasts 3 turns. Not 1, 2 or 4. 3!! If you want to STOP hauling butt, run into something.)

CARSON (Lumpin Lightfingers)

Race/Class: Muskrat Thief
Hit Points: 5 (40)

Speed: 4 (8)

Muscle: 3 (9)   **Zip:** 4 (8)
Smarts: 5 (8)   **Chutzpah:** 4 (11)

Shticks: Incredible Luck: 5 (Incredible Speed: 5)

Stuff: +10 Sword of Fiery Doom (3D+10 damage, plus starts fires), +6 Armor of Mighty Protection (+6 bonus is good vs all weapons, magical or otherwise, except thrown rocks or any attack by chipmunks), +4 Helmet of Sanity (Avoid being boggled on a 4 or less), Bag of Many Garage Sale Items (Contains stuff you might find at a garage sale), Potion of Invisibility (1 shot, lasts D+2 turns)

GILLY (Esmerelda the Energetic)

Race/Class: Human Sorceress   **Hit Points:** 6 (25)

Speed: 7 (7)

Shticks: Boggle with Cuteness: 8
Everlasting Perkiness: 10
(Magic Resistance: 9)
(Incredible Luck: 11)

Muscle: 5 (5)   **Zip:** 6 (9)
Smarts: 10 (11) **Chutzpah:** 7 (9)

Stuff: Staff of Bigtime Lightning Bolts (9 to use, does 5D+2 damage, 20 charges), Cloak of Many Fantasy RPG Things (8 to use, functions like a Bag of Many Things), Ring of Polymorphing (11 to use, works on self or others, lasts 3D+4 turns, 15 charges, Animator chooses the shape on a roll of 6 or less), +4 Silver Dagger (+4 to hit, does 1D+4 damage but does 4D+3 damage to werecreatures), Potion of Growth (1 dose, makes you grow to 3 times normal size, lasts 2D turns), Elixer of Garlic Breath (2 doses, do 2d+1 Stinky Garlic Breath Damage, lasts 3 turns)

Spells: Affect Fires (9) Exploding Ball Of Goo (7) Wall Of Spam (9) Fork In The Road (8) Stone To Oatmeal (9) False Dud Fireball (10) Light (10) Rapid Transit (7) Summon Terminator (6) Flower Power (7) Frank's Flying Fist (8) Wall of Peanut Butter (8) Detect Magic (10)

KEN (Brother Zork)

Race/Class: Human Priest   **Muscle:** 4 (6)   **Zip:** 6 (7)
Hit Points: 9 (30)   **Smarts:** 6 (10) **Chutzpah:** 5 (9)
Speed: 6 (8)   **Shticks:** Know Obscure Fact: 6

Stuff: +6 Holy Cudgel of Head Bonking (3D+6 damage), +4 Robe of Spell Turning (works on all spells except the ones he knows), Super Big Gulp Bottle of Holy Water (12 doses), Bottle of Healing Potion (heals 2D points of damage, 6 doses)

Spells: Bag O'Bees (8) Rampaging Rabbit (9) Friendliness (8) Wall Of Fog (10) Spring Rain (9) Protection (6) Holy Pimpslap (9) Greasy Spot (6) Light (10) Incredible Fiery Flatulence (8) Guacamoleball (8) Divine Blast of Seltzer (10)

IGOR (Sir Billingsly)

Race/Class: Human Fighter (though often mistaken for a half-orc berserker)
Hit Points: 7 (50)

Speed: 3 (6)
Muscle: 6 (10)   **Zip:** 3 (5)
Smarts: 4 (4)   **Chutzpah:** 3 (7)

Shticks: Know Obscure Fact: 5   (Talk To Monsters: 6)
(Incredible Strength: 9)

Stuff: +10 Sword of Chopping (4D+4 damage),+3 Armor of Arrow Turning (arrows continue on in random directions at full speed after it hits the armor. Arrows do 2D+3 damage), +3 Vorpal Axe (does +3 damage and gets a +4 to cut off heads), +2 Dagger (+2 damage), Boots of Doorkicking (+4 to kicking in doors), 3 bottles of Healing Potion (heals 3d6 points of damage), 3 bottles of Resurrection Oil (brings a character back from being Fallen Down, to a one hitpoint level), backpack full of junk food.

THE MIGHTY WARHAMSTER!
(and Carson the Muskrat)

Two new less-than-official special characters for Warhammer Fantasy Battles
(Also known as the Top Ten Signs I'm Reading Too Much Dork Tower)

by Tim Huckelberry • Games Workshop, USA

Profile	M	WS	BS	S	T	W	I	A	Ld
The Warhamster	5	5	5	4	4	2	6	3	9
Carson	5	2	2	2	2	1	3	1	6

Weapons and Armor: The Warhamster is armed with the Halberd of Mighty Slaying and wears the Armor of Sharp Spiky Bits. He also has the Gem of Really Scary Visions embedded in his right eye socket.

Carson is armed with his Lucky Spear and carries a Helmet and Shield. The latter two don't do anything special really, other than give him a 5+ Armor Save. Kinda boring, but there you go.

As special characters, both must be fielded exactly as presented, and cannot be given any additional equipment or weapons. Their points cost includes all weapons and equipment listed with them.

Dogs, er, Hamsters of War for hire! The Warhamster and Carson are a mercenary unit, willing to work for almost any army. They will count as a single Hero selection for a Dogs of War army. Alternatively, they can be hired as a Rare unit in other Warhammer armies, except for Bretonnia (much too full of themselves), any Chaos army (the Warhamster still has some standards, and they tried to eat Carson that one time), or High Elves (even more full of themselves than the Bretonnians). They can be taken as a Special unit in Dwarven armies, as both know at the least the beer will be first rate there.

Points: The Warhamster and Carson can be hired for oh, say, 175 points or so. Too high? For you, special deal - 165 points. Sound OK? You can deduct 5 points for every copy of Dork Tower you bring with you to the game for your opponent to read afterwards too, up to 25 points maximum though! And bringing the trade paperback will only count as one comic, but nice try there fanboy.

Special Rules:

Formation: The Warhamster and his faithful squire Carson can operate as a skirmishing unit of two models, or may join an existing unit following the same rules as Characters joining a unit. They must always either be within 2" of each other (if skirmishing) or placed side by side (if in a unit).

Ready for Anything: The team has a near suicidal bravery, largely due to the fact that so far nothing has killed them (so it must be working for them, right?). Both the Warhamster and Carson are immune to Psychology.

OUR HEROES:
The Warhamster: The Warhamster's real name was lost long ago to the mists of time. It is whispered though that he was once a lowly soldier in a forgotten army. After years of fighting he rose through the ranks to become a general himself. One day however, he dared question the orders of his sovereign king (said orders being to attack at dawn by charging uphill a thousand paces directly

due east through mud a foot deep). The king was incensed by this insubordination, and used his Bound Spell of Real Nasty Things to release one of his mightiest curses, twisting his former general's form into the present bestial shape. The king then lead his men on to a glorious fiasco which became the stuff of many a "Military Blunders" special on the History Channel.

Outcast now, the Warhamster was banished from the kingdom. However, his skills were still in demand, and he gained renown as an outstanding mercenary for hire. He now roams the Warhammer World striking fear in the hearts of pretentious and incompetent leaders on the battlefield.

Special Rules:

It Must Be Mine! Out there somewhere is the original magical item that cursed him into his present form, and since it was lost in battle it only stands to reason (for the Warhamster anyways) that if he fights enough battles, he can recover the item and undo the curse. He makes it a specialty to snare any magical items an enemy might have, to see if they are what he's looking for. So far, no such luck.

The upshot though is that before the first round of combat the Warhamster can make a special attack against one enemy in base contact. The player must shout out "It Must Be Mine!" in a loud voice, then may make the attack. Use the Warhamster's Initiative as if it was his Weapon Skill, and the enemy's Initiative as if it was his Weapon Skill. If the "hit" is successful, the Warhamster may snatch away one magic item from the enemy. It can only be an Arcane Item, Talisman, or Enchanted Item though. It cannot be a magic weapon or magic standard, as they are too big. It especially cannot be magic armor, as that would be difficult as well as probably embarrassing for both parties. The swiped item is then rendered useless for the rest of the game, as the Warhamster tosses it to the side in disgust. It wasn't what he was looking for, but

he'll keep trying...

Armor of Sharp Spiky Bits: The Warhamster's magical armor is covered with razor sharp extensions, designed to cut open anyone who gets too close! Unfortunately, this means friend as well as foe (though Carson has been around his boss long enough to always duck out of the way). All models in base contact with the Warhamster (except Carson) suffer a S3 automatic hit at the start of each Close Combat phase. This is worked out in the same manner as impact hits from a Chariot (ie., before any other attacks are made). The armor is made of only the finest enchanted Elven metals too, and gives the Warhamster an 4+ Armor Save with a built-in 5+ Ward Save.

Halberd of Mighty Slaying: This ancient and sharp and... aw, who's reading the fluff bits here anyways? I can say whatever I want here, and it won't make any difference. You're just going to skip to the stats, right? Spoilsport. The weapon counts as making a magical attack at +2 Strength. It also holds a bound minor Fire Ball spell (which works like a regular

151

Fire Ball, but only range 12"). The bound spell has a Power Level of 3. Satisfied? Geesh.

Gem of Really Scary Visions: This ruby-red gem gleams with unholy light, as if illuminated from within the empty socket of the Warhamster's right eye. With it, the mighty warrior can instill dread in all who secretly know they are really faking it as leaders, and probably leading their followers to their messy deaths. The gem causes Fear to all Hero level characters, and Terror to all Lord level characters (since the Principia Peterisimo dictates that the higher the rank, the more likely the chance of incompetence).

Carson the Muskrat Special Rules:

The Warhamster came across his now faithful companion many moons ago. This awesome encounter, a mythic clash of titans and surely the true stuff of legends, will be included in an upcoming Warhamster Cool Background Book (Volume IV, "The True Stuff of Legends").

Huzzah! Carson will always strike before thinking, which is also usually before his enemy has realized that the small furry creature before him in the

funny helmet is actually something to worry about. Carson will always strike first in any combat round, unless the enemy's ability to strike first is magical. And yes, you have to shout "Huzzah!" when striking. Loudly. Make the other guys in the room look up & wonder what the heck's your deal. Half the fun, right?

Nimble Little Guy. His small size and agile form make Carson very hard to hit. And he's just so darn cute too! All strikes at him in close combat or via a ranged missile attack will only hit on a D6 roll of 6 (if struck by any "hits automatically" weapons, they will only hit on a 4+).

Lucky Spear: This enchanted item is one of the most potent weapons in the Warhammer World. Legend has it that it was crafted by the Old Ones themselves right before the

Great Catastrophe, and that Sigmar himself used it in his apocryphal journeys after abdicating the throne. In the hands of a skilled warrior it can effortlessly cleave Greater Demons in two, shatter the World's Edge Mountains, or seal the rift in reality in the Chaos Wastelands.

Unfortunately, that's not the case here. Carson found it beside a lake half buried in the sand awhile back, and has been using it ever since. It does OK for him, and he calls it his lucky spear. In Carson's hands it still strikes as a magic weapon, but only (only!) adds +2 to his Strength and negates all saving throws of any kind. It also protects him from spells; they will only affect him on a D6 roll of 6.

John—

I was thinking:
"What if your characters didn't have such nice room mates...?"

and had to live in....

PUBLIC
TOWERS....

Joe

City of
Mud Bay
Housing
Authority

What if the DORK TOWER characters DIDN'T have such nice housemates? Yes, it's another installment of...

Public Towers

by Joe Sharpnack

This issue: let's see how many time Joe forces John to censor his work! (Hey, kids: can you count along with Uncle Expletive?)

AFTERWORD

I first met John in the fifth form when we were attending Rutherford Boy's Academy of Cotswolds-Upon-Kent. He could draw even back then. While the rest of we boys were choosing up sides for football (soccer), one could always find John crouching behind a tree with his legendary box of colours. Being an awkward and introverted child, John's school career was not one of glamour or sport, which was the way of boys at Rutherford. This is not to say that John was unpopular with his fellow classmates. In fact, he was president of the Royal Order of Dungeons and Dragons/Monty Python/Star Wars/Gamers Society. An association that has obviously had an enormous influence on his work to this day.

John eventually graduated from Rutherford and moved to the United States. Before he worked in editorial cartooning in Wisconsin, his first job led him to the New York offices of Vulgar and Kitsch Greeting Cards where he became an engraver, etching the line "I wuv you THIS much" onto the pedestals of "Ziggy" statuettes. John felt that his talents were severely under utilized there but stayed on for six months citing that "the hours are easy and the money's good."

Easy hours and good money are probably the two things that epitomize John's endeavors today. He discovered that after years of hard, honest, socially responsible but poorly-paying work as an editorial cartoonist, there was a bonanza of quick (easy hours) dough (good money) to be made by exploiting a small, vulnerable group of misfits...the gamers. Who better to bait a desperate subculture with ostensibly sympathetic comic book stories than one of their own kind? So with his legendary box of colours, John set out to dominate the ultimate niche publishing market: a socially awkward mob of outcasts with money to burn. DORK TOWER was born.

Eventually, the comic books became the backbone of John's now-sprawling multimedia empire, Dork Storm Press. The Publishing Division alone employs more than 750 "Dork Troopers" (as John calls them) in six different countries with a daily budget of over $18.

What's John's next project? A movie? A theme park? There's even been talk of a romantic comedy titled "I wuv you THIS much" based on John's days struggling in New York. Whatever the new project will be, you can bet your First Edition Mattel Luke Skywalker Action Figure (mint, in box) that it will be dorky.

Joe Sharpnack, Iowa City, IA
j.turbu@eudoramail.com

Joe Sharpnack is an editorial cartoonist whose work has been censored time and time again in the pages of Dork Tower. He is also responsible for the prank letter on page 163, and apparently forgot John gets to have the last word.

About the Author

John Kovalic was born in Manchester, England, in 1962.
Dork Tower began in SHADIS magazine in 1996, and the
multi-Origins award-nominated Dork Tower comic book
was launched in June 1998. The first issue sold out in
eight weeks to fantastic reviews and tremendous industry
buzz. John's award-winning editorial cartoons appear
everywhere from his hometown WISCONSIN STATE
JOURNAL and CAPITAL TIMES (Madison, WI) to the
NEW YORK TIMES and the WASHINGTON POST.
His other creations include SnapDragons and Newbies
(with Liz Rathke), Wild Life, Beached, the Unspeakable
Oaf and many others.

One of the first cartoonists to put their work on the
internet, his self-produced World Wide Web site,
kovalic.com, has received numerous national and
international kudos. If you ask him nicely, he'll tell you
how he helped create GAMES Magazine's 1999 Party
Game of the Year, the international best-selling, award-
winning "Apples to Apples." He may even tell you how
he once ended up in the pages of the National Enquirer.

His degree was in Economics with a minor in Astrophysics.
In his spare time, John searches for spare time.

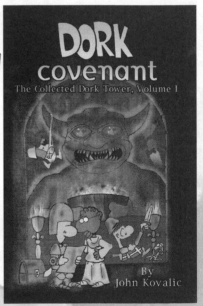

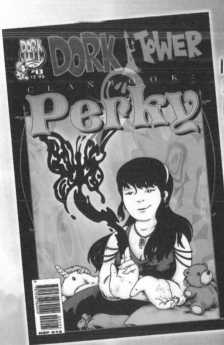

Dear Mr. ~~K~~ Dork,

My mom says I can't read you comic book anymore. She says you are like the devil.

Please tell her I can read them. I do not think you are like like the devil.

Thank you,

Mark

P.S. I really like the dog.

Evil is everywhere.